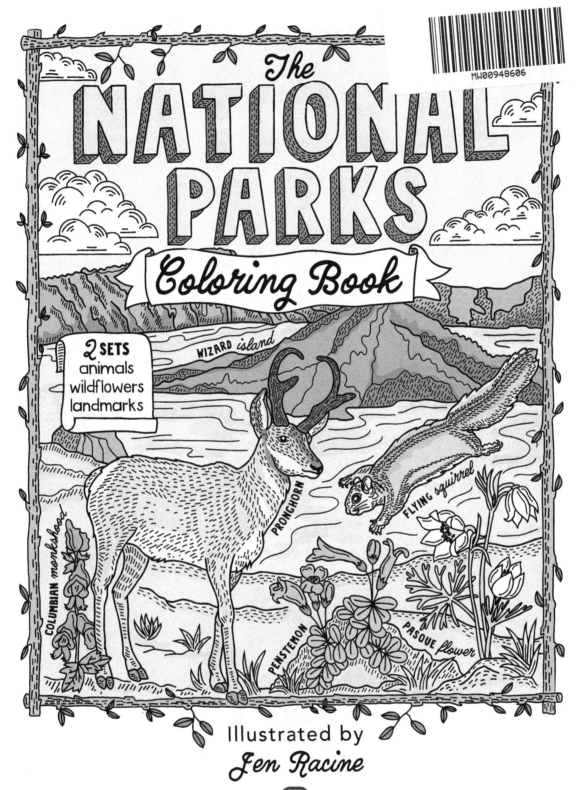

The NATIONAL PARKS

Coloring Book

2 SETS
animals
wildflowers
landmarks

WIZARD island

PRONGHORN

FLYING squirrel

COLUMBIAN monkshood

PENSTEMON

PASQUE flower

Illustrated by

Jen Racine

instagram: @jenracinecoloring

facebook.com/jenracinecoloring

www.jenracine.com

Other books by *Jen Racine*

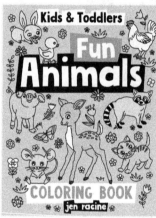

Go to
www.jenracine.com
and sign up for
FREE coloring pages!

Etsy Shop
www.etsy.com/shop/jenracinecoloring

Copyright © 2019 by Eclectic Esquire Media LLC
Published by Lake George Press

ISBN 978-1-7336959-4-7

National Parks in the USA

There are 58 National Parks in the USA. That's a lot of beautiful wide-open spaces with a huge variety of plants and animals! This coloring book highlights 24 of the most well-known National Parks.

IN THIS BOOK:

Acadia – *maine*
Arches – *utah*
Bryce Canyon – *utah*
Crater Lake – *oregon*
Denali – *alaska*
Everglades – *florida*
Glacier – *montana*
Grand Canyon – *arizona*
Grand Teton – *wyoming*
Great Smoky Mountains – *tennessee*
Hawai'i Volcanoes – *hawaii*
Hot Springs – *arkansas*
Isle Royale – *michigan*
Joshua Tree – *california*
Mammoth Cave – *kentucky*
Mesa Verde – *colorado*
Olympic – *washington*
Rocky Mountain – *colorado*
Saguaro – *arizona*
Sequoia – *california*
Shenandoah – *virginia*
Yellowstone – *wyoming*
Yosemite – *california*
Zion – *utah*

MORE NATIONAL PARKS:

Alaska
Gates of the Arctic
Glacier Bay
Katma
Kenai Fjords
Kobuk Valley
Lake Clark
Wrangell-St. Elias

National Park of American Samoa

Arizona
Petrified Forest

California
Channel Islands
Death Valley
Kings Canyon
Lassen Volcanic
Redwood

Colorado
Black Canyon of the Gunnison
Great Sand Dunes

Florida
Biscayne
Dry Tortugas

Hawaii
Haleakalā

Minnesota
Voyageurs

Nevada
Great Basin

New Mexico
Carlsbad Caverns

North Dakota
Theodore Roosevelt

Ohio
Cuyahoga Valley

South Carolina
Congaree

South Dakota
Badlands
Wind Cave

Texas
Big Bend
Guadalupe Mountains

United States Virgin Islands
Virgin Islands

Utah
Canyonlands
Capitol Reef

Washington
Mount Rainier
North Cascades

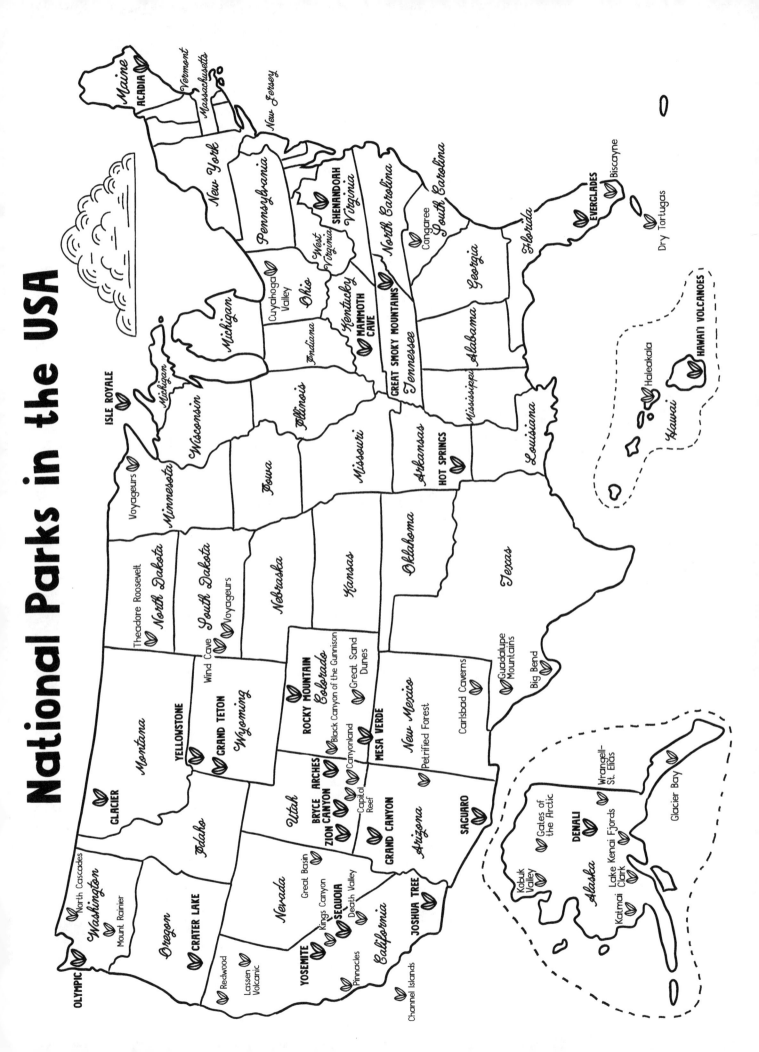

National Parks in the USA

Wildflower *Color Key*

ACADIA
- Pink Lady Slipper-*pale pink*
- Rhodora-*pink-purple*

ARCHES
- Yucca Plant-*pale yellow flower*
- Prickly Pear Cactus-*yellow flower*

BRYCE CANYON
- Bryce Canyon Paintbrush-*bright pink*
- Rabbitbrush-*bright yellow*

CRATER LAKE
- Columbian Monkshood-*bright yellow*
- Penstemon-*deep purple blue*
- Pasque Flower-*blue-purple*

DENALI
- White Arctic Mountain Heather-*white*
- Alaskan Mountain Avens-*white*

EVERGLADES
- American White Water Lily-*white*
- Clamshell Orchid-*dark purple-red*

GLACIER
- Purple Aster-*bright purple*
- Beargrass-*white*

GREAT SMOKY MOUNTAINS
- Wild Blue Phlox-*pale blue*
- Showy Orchis-*purple top, white*

GRAND CANYON
- Barrel Cactus-*yellow flower*
- Organ Pipe Cactus-*white flower*
- Saguaro Cactus-*white flower*

GRAND TETON
- Skyrocket Gilia-*bright red*
- Larkspur-*bright blue*

HAWAI'I VOLCANOES
- Mauna Loa Silversword-*yellow flower*

HOT SPRINGS
- Bee Balm-*bright pink*
- Spleenwort-*lime green*

ISLE ROYALE
- Calypso Orchid-*purple top, white*
- Skunk Cabbage-*pale yellow flower*

JOSHUA TREE
- Jumping Cholla Cactus-*pale yellow*
- California Poppy-*bright orange*

MAMMOTH CAVE
- Fire Pink-*bright pink-red*
- Wood Lily-*orange*

MESA VERDE
- Rock Goldenrod-*bright yellow*
- Evening Primrose-*pale yellow*

OLYMPIC
- Scottish Bluebell-*soft blue*
- Salal-*white flower*

ROCKY MOUNTAIN
- Rocky Mountain Columbine-*pale blue*
- Mountain Iris-*pale blue*

SAGUARO
- Saguaro Cactus-*light green*

SEQUOIA (& KINGS CANYON)
- Pacific Bleeding Heart-*pale pink*
- Meadow Lupine-*purple-blue*

SHENANDOAH
- Bloodroot-*white flower*
- Hepatica-*pale purple*

YELLOWSTONE
- Indian Paintbrush-*orange-red*

YOSEMITE
- Yosemite Aster-*pale purple*
- Fireweed-*bright pink*
- Columbine-*red & yellow*

ZION
- Salmon Globe Mallow-*yellow-orange*
- Sacred Datura-*white flower*

WESTERN *hemlock*

WIZARD *island*

FLYING *squirrel*

PRONGHORN

COLUMBIAN *monkshood*

PENSTEMON

PASQUE *flower*

CRATER LAKE

oregon

ROSEATE *spoonbill*

CLAMSHELL *orchid*

FLORIDA *cooter*

AMERICAN *alligator*

BALD *cypress*

AMERICAN WHITE *water lily*

EVERGLADES *florida*

DUSTY STAR *mountain*

MOUNTAIN *goat*

BEARGRASS

WOLVERINE

PURPLE *aster*

GLACIER

montana

CALIFORNIA *condor*

RINGTAIL *cat*

SAGUARO *cactus*

ORGAN PIPE *cactus*

BARREL *cactus*

GRAND CANYON

arizona

WILD BLUE *phlox*

WHITE-TAILED *deer*

SHOWY *orchis*

WOODCHUCK

GREAT SMOKY MOUNTAINS

tennessee

KILAUEA

PAHOEHOE *lava*

MAUNA LOA *silversword*

HAWAIIAN GREEN *sea turtle*

HAWAIIAN *goose* (Nēnē)

HAWAI'I VOLCANOES

hawaii

GRAY *wolf*

RED *squirrel*

CALYPSO *orchid*

SKUNK *cabbage*

ISLE ROYALE

michigan

INDIANA *bat*

STALACTITES

KENTUCKY CAVE *shrimp*

STALAGMITES

WOOD *lily*

FIRE *pink*

RACOON

MAMMOTH CAVE

kentucky

STONY MAN cliffs

BLACK bear

SPOTTED skunk

BLOODROOT

HEPATICA

SHENANDOAH

virginia

OLD FAITHFUL *inn*

GRAND PRISMATIC *hot spring*

AMERICAN *bison*

OLD FAITHFUL *gyser*

INDIAN *paintbrush*

PIKA

YELLOWSTONE

wyoming

BASS HARBOR *lighthouse*

PEREGRINE *falcon*

ATLANTIC *puffin*

RIVER *otter*

RHODORA

PINK LADY *slipper*

ACADIA

maine

ROSEATE *spoonbill*

CLAMSHELL *orchid*

FLORIDA *cooter*

AMERICAN *alligator*

AMERICAN WHITE *water lily*

BALD *cypress*

EVERGLADES *florida*

KILAUEA

PAHOEHOE *lava*

MAUNA LOA *silversword*

HAWAIIAN GREEN *sea turtle*

HAWAIIAN *goose* (Nēnē)

HAWAI'I VOLCANOES

hawaii

GRAY *wolf*

RED *squirrel*

CALYPSO *orchid*

SKUNK *cabbage*

ISLE ROYALE

michigan

LONGS *peak*

QUAKING *aspen*

ROCKY MOUNTAIN *elk*

ROCKY MOUNTAIN *columbine*

MOUNTAIN *iris*

BEAVER

ROCKY MOUNTAIN
colorado

PETROGLYPHS

SAGUARO *cactus*

JAVELINA

BOBCAT

SAGUARO

arizona

STONY MAN cliffs

BLACK bear

SPOTTED skunk

BLOODROOT

HEPATICA

SHENANDOAH

virginia

OLD FAITHFUL *inn*

GRAND PRISMATIC *hot spring*

AMERICAN *bison*

OLD FAITHFUL *gyser*

INDIAN *paintbrush*

PIKA

YELLOWSTONE

wyoming

HALF dome

SIERRA NEVADA big horn sheep

YOSEMITE aster

columbine

fireweed

ALPINE chipmunk

YOSEMITE

california

CPSIA information can be obtained
at www.ICGtesting.com
Printed in the USA
BVHW090918210820
586920BV00016B/18

9 781733 695947